GRADED COURSE
FOR DRUM KIT

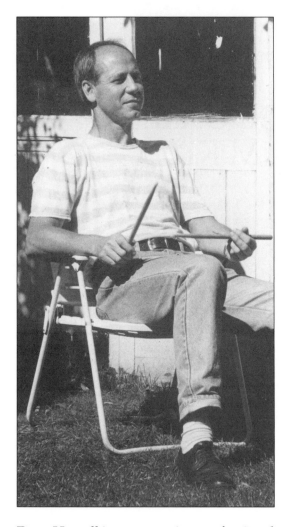

Dave Hassell is a very active professional drummer and percussionist having played almost every style of music from funk, rock, jazz, cabaret, club dates, folk to orchestral. Since the mid 1970's he has worked mainly as a session musician recording for T.V., radio, the film and record industries and commercials. Live music engagements include playing with many notable British and American jazz artists and he leads one of Britain's foremost Latin bands APITOS. As well as conducting Latin workshops throughout the country he is involved with Jazz College and teaches at their annual Summer School. He is currently a member of the music faculties of Salford College of Technology and The Royal Northern College of Music in Manchester.

GRADED COURSE FOR DRUM KIT

BY
DAVE HASSELL

BOOK 2

WOODSMOOR PRESS

Acknowledgements and grateful thanks to:

Mel Dean	composer/keyboards/guitar
Derek Hilton	composer/keyboards
Richie Close	keyboards
Dave Lynane	string bass
Pete Glennon	bass guitar
Dave Hassell	percussion

Recorded at Commercial Sound Studio, Manchester © 1989

To buy Faber Music publications or to find out about the full range of titles available,
please contact your local music retailer or Faber Music sales enquiries:

Faber Music Ltd, Burnt Mill, Elizabeth Way, Harlow, CM20 2HX England
Tel: +44(0)1279 82 89 82   Fax: +44(0)1279 82 89 83
sales@fabermusic.com   fabermusic.com

When I was asked whether I would be interested in writing a book that could be used to help students prepare for a graded examination for drums I asked myself 'How do you examine the modern drummer?' Unlike other instrumentalists I feel a drummer should not be examined alone in a room without the accompaniment of other musicians. To do so would be placing the student in a false playing environment, therefore not centreing in on the basic requirements of the modern drummer, which are in my opinion;

1. *The ability to interpret the drum chart whilst understanding the musical concept, and*
2. *Listening to all that is happening around, responding accordingly.*

This last attribute is the key to producing a mature and musical performance, as the understanding of one's role can be considered to be the prime aspect of musicianship. As one of the all- time great drummers, Jo Jones, said 'If you learn to listen you got the best seat in the house'.

The following time patterns are designed to give the student a fairly comprehensive knowledge of the rhythms expected of the professional drummer. The lists are by no means complete, but I feel they will give the serious player a good foundation on which to build. The student must keep an open mind and be constantly listening to all forms of music in a wide variety of styles – this will provide a musical vocabulary which can be called upon at any time. LISTEN AND LEARN. Go out and watch as many professional musicians as possible; be like a sponge and absorb what they have to say.

One of the essential attributes of the modern drummer is the ability to make the other musicians around feel comfortable, by being sensitive, creative, solid and at all times in control. Another attribute which is seldom mentioned is PATIENCE! One must have the patience to stay with the requirement of the music.

There could be criticism that the following drum parts are too open (solo – – –) and that there should be more written solos within the arrangements. All I can say is that, judging by my own many years of experience playing all kinds of music from Jingles to Jazz, Orchestral to Punk, I have only come across written drum solos on very few occasions. Even then the M.D. was not particularly bothered whether or not I played the written solo just so long as what I did remained in context with the music. INTERPRETATION is the key word. To date there have been no set rules on how we play the drum charts/guides and because of the nature of the instrument I don't think there ever will be. DRUMS ARE UNIQUE in that most of the time the interpretation is left to the drummer's creativity and musicianship. Give five drummers the same part and you end up with five different versions.

This is not meant to be a 'How to do it' book because there are many fine tuition books on the market that cover every aspect of drumming. It is intended to be more a source of practical material for the benefit of the student and teacher alike. I hope you will get as many hours of pleasure from studying this material as I had in preparing it. Remember, being a musician is a life time's endeavour and one that is never mastered.

Dave Hassell

I

The following exercises are to be played at all speeds (slow-fast). Be sure the tempo you choose suits the rhythm and feels comfortable and musical. They are intended to be played for a minimum of two minutes, at varying dynamic levels. 'Use your own judgement - start making decisions now!' Include your own stops and starts within the patterns themselves, always mentally adhering to the basic pulse. I recommend that you play the patterns with and without the aid of a metronome. Only when you think rhythms sound and feel comfortable - swing or groove - should you be satisfied and move on.

I would strongly advise any drummers who are serious about their art to constantly review and practise simple time patterns. At the end of the day it is the ability to play steady swinging time musically that results in success.

It is possible to substitute these time patterns for the written parts in the following pieces. A more simplistic or difficult rhythm may therefore be used within an arrangement, and blank staves have ben left for you to write down individual ideas. You should experiment and use imagination and musicianship to find out which patterns work. DEVELOP GOOD LISTENING HABITS. This will prepare for the time when you are asked not play the written part, but to improvise with something that will fit into the tune. The sooner you get into the habit of thinking for yourself and are not afraid to experiment or make decisions, the sooner you will be on the first rung of the ladder, and with hard work, talent, and luck will rise to great heights in this wonderful art form.

ALTERNATIVE TIME PATTERNS

Fast Country ♩ = 140

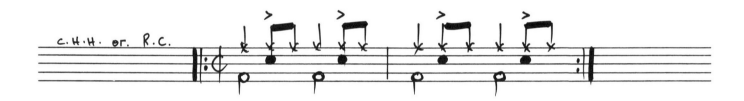

Funk

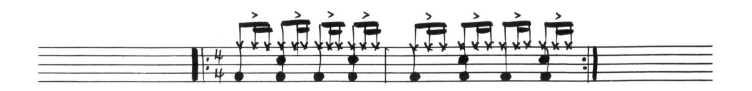

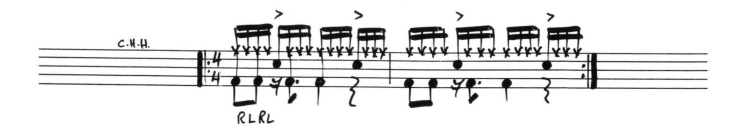

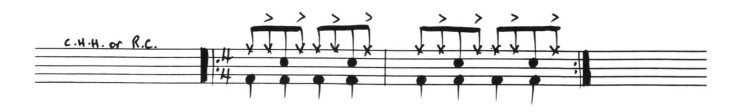

ALL THE EXERCISES
ON THIS PAGE CAN
BE PLAY ON THE.
C.H·H or R.C.
WHEN PLAYING ON
R.C. ADD THE H·H
TO THE 2 AND 4 BEATS.
OR ON ALL FOUR BEATS.

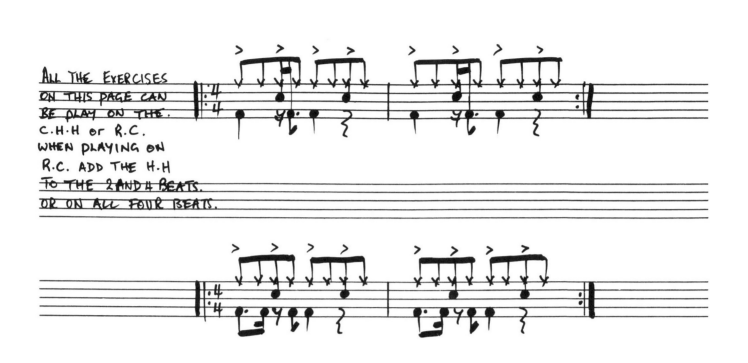

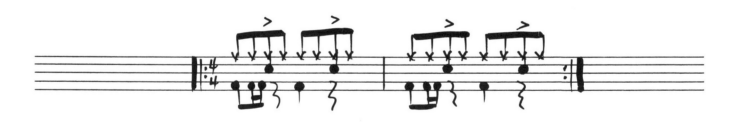

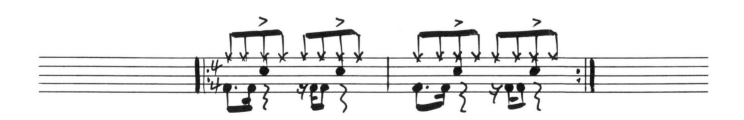

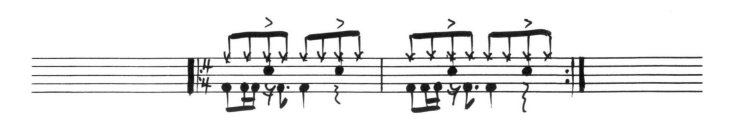

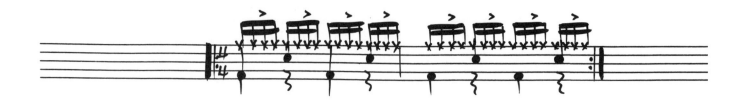

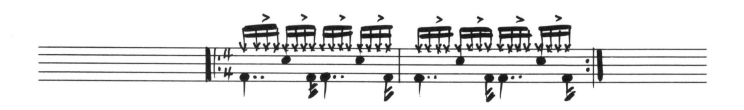

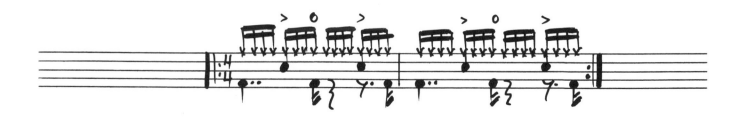

Funk / Rock

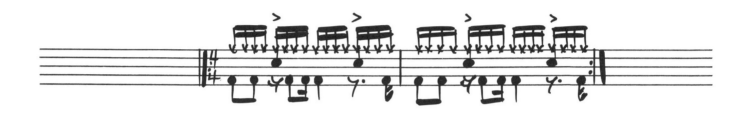

Swing 4 Beat

Swing 2 Beat

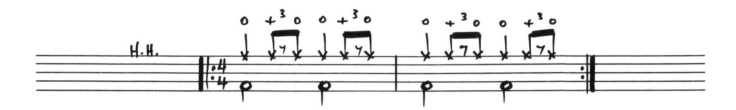

Spanish Tango

Argentinean Tango

Mambo

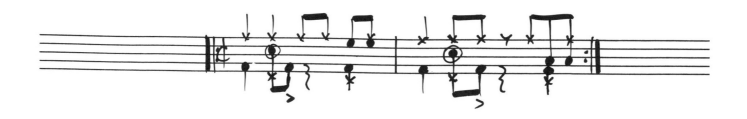

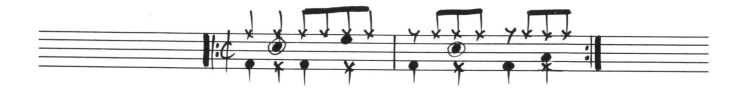

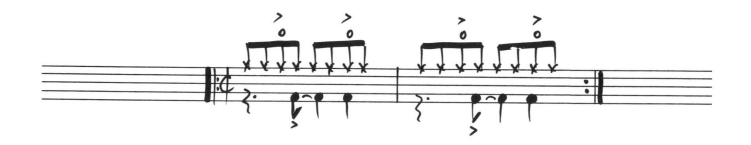

Pasa Doble

Reggae One Drop

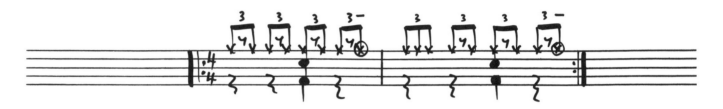

Reggae Four Drop

Show

Jazz Waltz

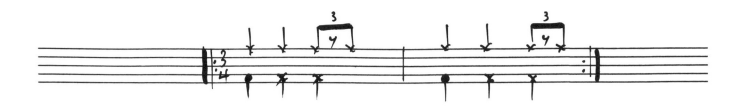

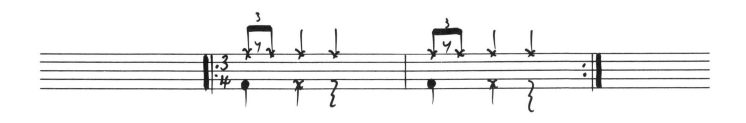

Calypso

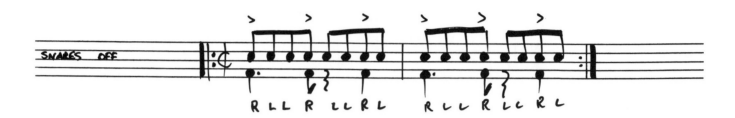

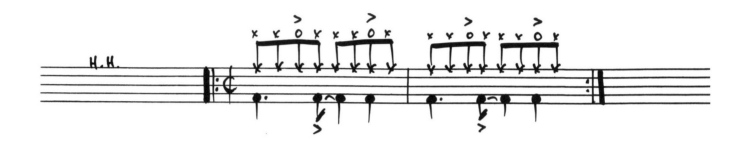

Calypso (Soca)

Mambo Show

Funk Shuffle

Samba

Afro Cuban (Nanigo)

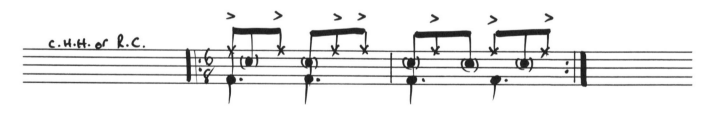

3/4 Rock

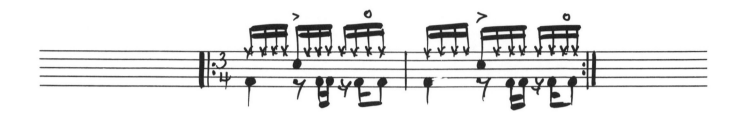

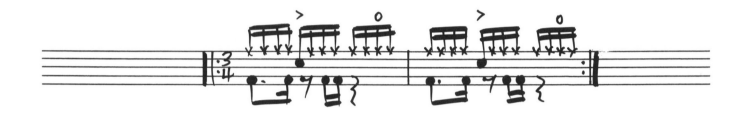

5/4 Rock

Jazz 5/4

7/4 Rock

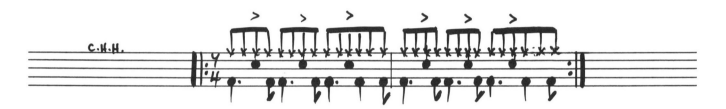

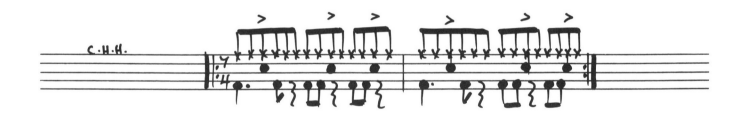

5/8 Rock

7/8 Rock

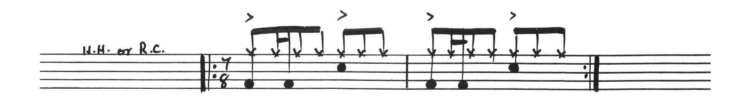

GENERAL INSTRUCTIONS

Listen to the tape following the drum part, but do NOT play.

Check the repeats and DS al coda, and make a mental note of any difficult bars.

Play the part along with the tape. Play time (ie. basic beats) through the difficult bars and practise these separately until you can play them fluently.

Then play the arrangement as written - musically and with taste, always listening to yourself.

I recommend the use of headphones when playing along with the tape, but BEWARE! Do not have the volume too loud and do not wear the headphones for too long - it is very easy to do permanent damage to your hearing. You may prefer to wear one side on the ear and the other off, this will then allow you to hear the subtleties and intricacies of the drum patterns you are playing.

I strongly advise that you study the following pieces with a competent drum teacher.

Key

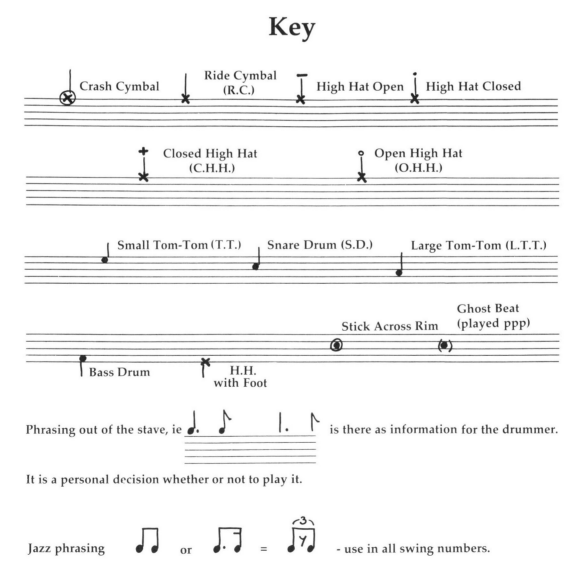

CONTENTS

No.24 FAST COUNTRY

No.25 FUNK ONE

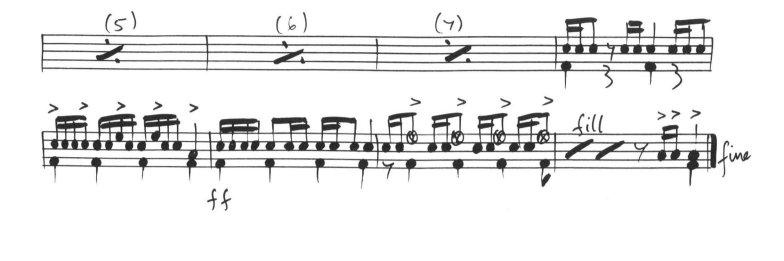

No.26 FUNK TWO

No.27 SWING FAST

No.28 SWING TWO BEAT FAST

No.29   SPANISH TANGO

No.30 ARGENTINEAN TANGO

fine

No.31 MAMBO

No.32 PASA DOBLE

No.33 REGGAE ONE DROP

No.34 REGGAE FOUR DROP

22

No.35   SHOW TEMPO FAST

No.36 JAZZ WALTZ

27

No.37 CALYPSO

No.38　DISCO FEEL

30

No.39 MAMBO SHOW

No.40 FUNK SHUFFLE

No.41 SAMBA

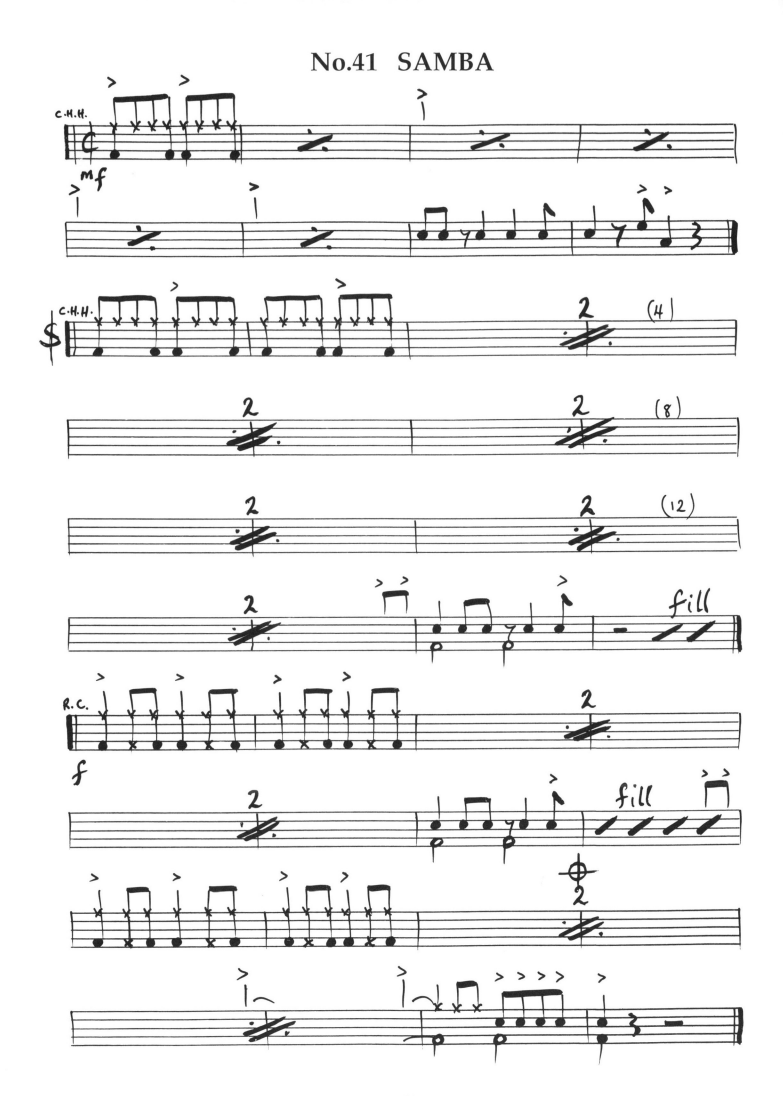

No.42   AFRO CUBAN (NANIGO)

No.43 3/4 ROCK

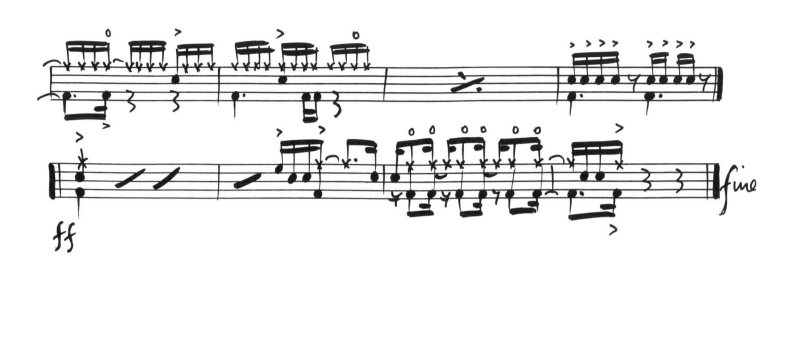

No.44   5/4 ROCK

No.45   5/4 JAZZ

No.46   7/4 ROCK

No.47 5/8 ROCK

49

No.48 7/8 ROCK

Independence Studies Chart 1

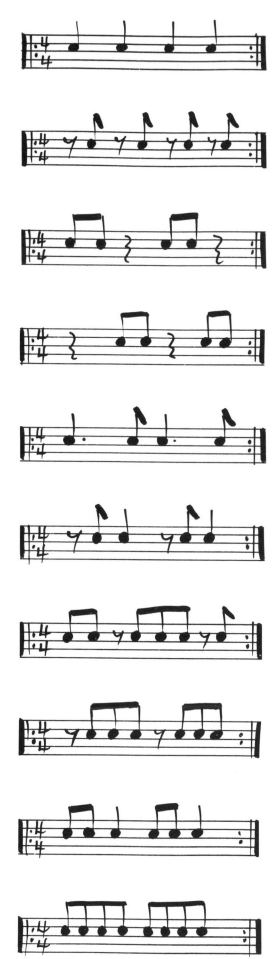

① RIDE CYMBAL PATTERNS

a)

b)

② TO BE PLAYED ON

a)   Snare Drum

b)   Bass Drum

c)   Hi-Hat (with foot)

⎫ against R.C.

③ H.H. WITH FOOT.

a)

b)

⎫ against R.C.

④ Snare drum plays figures
Bass drum fills in rests,
completing a continuous
Quaver/⅛ note pattern.

<u>i.e.</u>

S.D (figure)

B.D (fill in)

H.H. to play a) or b)

R.C. to play a) or b)

Independence Studies Chart 2

④ Snare drum plays figures—
Bass drum fills in rests,
Completing a continuous
triplet pattern

i.e.

S.D

B.D
(fill in)

H.H.   to play a) or b)

R.C.   to play a) or b)

RECOMMENDED READING

Jim Blackley	*Syncopated Rolls for the Modern Drummer*	Jim Blackley
Ralph Humphrey	*Even In The Odds*	C.L. Barnhouse
Gary Chester	*The New Breed*	Modern Drummer
Mel Lewis/Clem Derosa	*It's Time*	Kendor Music
Birger Sülsbruck	*Latin American Percussion*	Hanson
Airto	*The Spirit of Percussion*	21st Century Publications
Ed Thigpen	*The Sound of Brushes*	E. Thigpen Action Reaction
Philly Joe Jones	*Brush Artistry*	Premier Drum Co.
Joe Morello	*Master Studies*	Modern Drummer
Louis Bellson	*Modern Reading Text in 4/4*	Belwyn Mills
Frank Chico Guerrero	*Latin Sounds from the Drum Set*	Pro Drum Shop
Morris Goldenberg	*Modern School for Snare Drum*	Chappell
Bob Moses	*Drum Wisdom*	Modern Drummer
Ted Reed	*Syncopation for the Modern Drummer*	Ted Reed
Ed Soph	*Essential Techniques for the Drum Set*	Meredith Music
Peter Erskine	*Drum Concepts and Techniques*	21st Century Publications
Jamey Aebersold	*Books and Tapes - Play-Along*	Jamey Aebersold

RECOMMENDED LISTENING

JAZZ - Big Band

Count Basie
Duke Ellington
Maynard Ferguson
Bob Florence
Woody Herman
Thad Jones/Mel Lewis
Rob McConnell

JAZZ - Small Group

Chick Corea
Miles Davies
Stan Getz
Herbie Hancock
Keith Jarrett
Oscar Peterson
Sonny Rollins
Steps Ahead
McCoy Tyner

LATIN

Airto
Ray Barretto
Pete Escovedo
Irakere
Tito Puente

ROCK

The Beatles
Chuck Berry
James Brown
Ray Charles
Joe Cocker
Ry Cooder
Steely Dan
Michael Jackson
Bob James
Elton John
B.B. King
Robert Palmer
Elvis Presley
Lee Ritenour
Sly & Robbie
Rush
To-To
Peter Tosh
Stevie Wonder
Led Zeppelin